CATALOGUE TWENTY

SUN PICTURES

JULIA MARGARET CAMERON

Text by Larry J. Schaaf

HANS P. KRAUS JR.   FINE PHOTOGRAPHS

NEW YORK

The exhibition *Julia Margaret Cameron*
will be on view October 4 – November 18, 2011.
Monday – Friday, noon – 6 P.M. and by appointment.

The authenticity of each item is guaranteed.
Measurements are given in centimeters with height before width.

Prices will be quoted on request
for those items which are not sold or reserved.

Unless otherwise noted, titles of the photographs
and copyright dates are taken from the catalogue raisonné by
Julian Cox and Colin Ford, *Julia Margaret Cameron, The Complete
Photographs* (Los Angeles: The J. Paul Getty Museum, 2003)
and citations are abbreviated: Cox & Ford.

FRONTISPIECE
HENRY HERSCHEL HAY CAMERON
(English, 1856–1911)
Julia Margaret Cameron
Carbon print, circa 1870. 25.5 x 21.8 cm mounted on 39.8 x 29.5 cm card.
"Autotype" blindstamp. Facsimile signature on mount.
Provenance: Jackson-Vaughan family, by descent.

HANS P. KRAUS JR. INC.
since 1984
OLD MASTERS OF PHOTOGRAPHY

———————————————————————

962 PARK AVENUE, NEW YORK, NEW YORK 10028
212-794-2064   info@sunpictures.com   www.sunpictures.com

———————————————————————

OPEN BY APPOINTMENT

Julia Margaret Cameron (1815–1879) ranks among the great portrait artists. Taking up photography at the age of 48, Cameron defied convention and with her unique aesthetic vision, established her own distinctive style. Living and working within a broad intellectual and creative society, she portrayed writers, scientists, and artists, as well as parlor maids and visitors to the Isle of Wight. Widely exhibited in her day, Cameron's work was praised by many, but it infuriated others. Curiously, painters and the general public accepted her style of photography more readily than did many of her photographic colleagues.

Unlike the fate suffered by the work of most of her contemporaries, Cameron's photographs never went out of fashion. They have always been viewed with interest, and have been published and exhibited continuously from Cameron's era to the present. Her vision shares a sensibility with Pre-Raphaelite paintings, and she is rightfully included in nearly all retrospective exhibitions about that movement. Modern artists continue to be inspired by her photographs.

The majority of the items in this catalogue come from a special source. Mrs. Cameron's niece Adeline Maria Jackson married Professor Henry Halford Vaughan, and together they retained a collection of prints given to them by her aunt. Many of these photographs carry personal inscriptions. All have been preserved within the family until now.

Julia Margaret Cameron is one of the four pillars of British photography. William Henry Fox Talbot, Hill & Adamson, and Roger Fenton have previously been the subjects of *Sun Pictures* monographs. It is with pleasure that I devote my twentieth *Sun Pictures* catalogue to the work of this timeless photographer.

HPK Jr.

Julia Margaret Cameron

INTRODUCTION

Mrs. Cameron was the first person who had the wit to see that her mistakes were her successes ...[1]

In 1815, the year after Waterloo, Julia Margaret Pattle was born in Calcutta, India. Her father was a distinguished if rakish East India Company official, her mother the elegant daughter of French Royalists. Educated in France and Britain, convalescence took her from India to the Cape of Good Hope, where she was introduced to Sir John Herschel, who would figure mightily in her life. Perhaps more importantly, there she also met Charles Hay Cameron (1795–1881), a jurist, liberal reformer, and intellectual who wrote *On the Sublime and Beautiful*.[2] They married in 1838 and a decade later retired to Tunbridge Wells, Kent. By 1850, they had moved to London, where Julia entered into an active, almost bohemian, intellectual life, which included joining the Arundel Society, founded by John Ruskin and others to educate and improve public taste in art. In 1860, while her husband tended to their coffee plantations in Ceylon, Julia visited the poet laureate, Alfred, Lord Tennyson at Farringford, in Freshwater, the Isle of Wight. She immediately and impulsively bought two cottages there, becoming Tennyson's next-door neighbor. Within a decade, she had them joined by a central tower in the Gothic style, and named the grand edifice Dimbola, after the family estate in Ceylon (see illus. p. 9).[3] It was to become the locus of a most extraordinary photographic career. "The life at Freshwater and at Farringford in the days when the houses were few ... was a life peculiar to the place, quiet and self-contained, completely out of the world, and yet at the same time in touch with its larger interests ... some of the people who came to the Bay did not write books, but lived them."[4]

In many cases, artists are figures of mystery—clearly brilliant, obviously inspirational, obscure to a fault. In contrast, Julia Margaret Cameron left us a rich legacy, not only of her art, but also of the collective memories of the people she influenced. She inspired not only biographers, but also writers and historians. Her great-niece Virginia Woolf observed that she "had a gift of ardent speech and picturesque behaviour which has impressed itself upon the calm pages of Victorian biography."[5] Reviewing Cameron's photographs and life,

Alvin Langdon Coburn apologized: "I could ramble on indefinitely concerning the exploits of this valiant lady; a book, and no less, it would take to do her full justice, and a book I hope one day to write about her, with pictures on every second page."[6] Sadly, that book by the master photographer and critic was never written, but much else has been in the intervening years. The already rich literature on Cameron has recently been enhanced, and her works have been analyzed and codified by a catalogue raisonné, an essential form of art reference only beginning to be used in the study of photography.[7]

What defines a Cameron photograph? She entered into photography at an awkward point in the development of the new art. Gone was the first flush of experimentation, when pioneers such as William Henry Fox Talbot were still probing the technology. Gone was the innocence that allowed early photographers such as David Octavius Hill & Robert Adamson to explore an art form before it had any rules. By the 1860s, the first great wave of amateur photographers had organized into societies, met regularly, made rules, hung exhibitions, published journals, and in the process began stagnating. A robust commercial portrait market raised expectations in customers and promoted conventions in posing and lighting. Julia Margaret Cameron adhered to none of this. She strove to make her heads life-size, and, if anything, her fuller figures seem larger-than-life, even within the physical constraints of her format. For better or for worse, her photographs have always been showstoppers in any exhibition. They are unlike the work of her contemporaries, and perhaps are more often echoed in modern photography. Big, bold, and penetrating, they are at the same time incredibly natural, indeed comfortable, to behold. "Amateurs are not as a rule successful in portrait-taking, but we must make an exception in favor of a lady, Mrs. Cameron, whose life-size portraits ... are taken with the large lens, and, without the appearance of art, are yet most artistic portraits. The head of Alfred Tennyson, with its flowing locks, and calm, grand expression, shows us the power of photography in large—if we may so speak. Mrs. Cameron has a fine sense of light and shade, and the heads she has taken remind us of the noble penciling of Correggio, so grandly are the masses of light and shade disposed."[8] The beautiful simplicity of Cameron's compositions belies their wonderfully complex underpinnings, for the truth and clarity in them emerges from the contradictions of the woman herself. In her day, her work was perhaps better understood by traditional artists and the general public than by members of the photographic community.

The President of The Photographic Society of Scotland, Sir David Brewster, welcomed Cameron into membership in December 1864. Less than two months later, reviewing Cameron's submissions to the Society's exhibition, *The Photographic Journal* declared, "Mrs. Cameron exhibits her series of out-of-focus portraits of celebrities. We must give this lady credit for daring originality, but at the expense of all other photographic qualities ... in these pictures, all that is good in photography has been neglected and the shortcomings of the art are prominently exhibited."[9] In contrast, the more broadly based *Intellectual Observer* considered some of her early exhibited work and concluded, "Another common photographic defect is giving too much prominence to detail, as the early artists did, and as the modern Pre-Raphaelites continue to do. Mrs. Cameron has advanced photography beyond this stage ... she has introduced breadth and generalization; her contrasts are strong, but not violent, and she has been singularly successful with half-tones. The qualities we have mentioned belong to what we may call the technical, or manipulative branch of art; and they are essentials to success; but something more is wanted: a true work of art is also a work of mind, and Mrs. Cameron has rescued photography from mere copying."[10] In her obituary, *The Times* cited "her perfectly original and unique photographic work ... which after a daring fashion of her own, forfeiting the sharpness and definition which ordinary photographers strive for, and which is one of the things artists most dislike in photographic portraiture ... she produced ... the most picture-like photographs certainly which have been given to the world."[11]

The forces that shaped Cameron's photography were the same ones that shaped her life. Already an influential member of society in India, Julia's move to Britain brought her into closer contact with artists, writers, and poets. When she moved to London, this circle expanded further. Her younger sister Sarah married Henry Thoby Prinsep and in January 1851 took over Little Holland House, then in rural London, less than three miles from Cameron's house. Another sister, Virginia, had married Viscount Eastnor, a photographer admired by Henry Talbot and soon to be Vice President of the Photographic Society of London.[12] The three sisters so often held court at Little Holland House that it became known as "Pattledom" or the "Kingdom of Pattle," attracting a wide range of writers, poets, intellectuals, and Pre-Raphaelite painters. It was here that the various strands of Julia's life began to intertwine more tightly, ones that would eventually influence her photographs. The sisters "had unconventional rules for life, which excellently suited themselves, and which also interested and stimulated other people. They were unconscious artists, divining beauty and living with it. It was this charming gift, this courage of good taste in Mrs. Cameron, that gave her so much success in photography."[13]

The social circles into which Cameron was drawn at Little Holland House were complex, not so much changing as continuously developing new cross-linkages. While painters and other visual artists were an important part of her life, Cameron's photographic references leaned more towards poets and writers. The reclusive Alfred Tennyson became one of her closest friends and most ardent supporters. The origins of his relationship with Cameron can be partially traced to Lady Charlotte Elizabeth Guest, née Bertie (1812–1895). An avid reader from childhood and fiercely self-educated, Lady Charlotte became the youthful English bride to a successful Welsh entrepreneur.[14] She taught herself not only Welsh, a difficult enough feat in itself, but also its medieval roots, and became an important translator of early Welsh songs and fables, publishing the critical translation of the *Mabinogion* starting in 1838.[15] This became part of the underpinning for Tennyson's *The Idylls of the King*, which in turn was a major source of inspiration for Cameron.[16] Lady Charlotte and Julia found a shared intellectual resonance in the richly textured imaginary world of King Arthur. One senses that even in a crowded room they would have sought each other out for conversation. "Julia Margaret Cameron recalled the evocative effects of a reading" of a medieval tale at Lady Charlotte's Canford Manor in Dorset.[17] Cameron considered it "one of the loveliest houses" in England "with holiday and midnight revelry all the twenty-four hours around."[18] Little Holland House was next door to Exeter House, the Guests' other home in London.[19] "Late one summer night when Lady Charlotte was in bed, her neighbor Julia arrived at her house with Tennyson. Meeting Lady Charlotte at the garden gate they persuaded her to return to the Cameron's 'to see how nicely I have converted my conservatory into a sitting room for Alfred.' Tennyson placed his large black sombrero on Lady Charlotte's head and later presented her with a signed copy of *The Idylls of the King*."[20] At the age of 74, Lady Charlotte took photography lessons in order to better understand the process of copying her collections, reasoning that if Cameron could start at the age of 48, it was not too late for her.[21]

Unche Charles & Aunt Julia's house at FreshWater Bay — Isle of Wight.

Unknown photographer. *Dimbola Lodge, Isle of Wight*
Albumen print from a collodion negative, 1871. 18.0 x 23.8 cm mounted on 26.7 x 36.2 card.
Provenance: Jackson-Vaughan family, by descent. Cox & Ford, fig. 22

In spite of intense scrutiny, we can confirm surprisingly little of Cameron's start in photography. It was Sir John Herschel who first alerted her to the new art in 1842, while she was still in India. Subsequently she was as aware of photography as anyone in artistic circles would have been, but more engaged than most, even before she became a photographer herself. She participated in compiling several significant albums of early photography, hired some photographers and cajoled others (such as Oscar Gustav Rejlander) into taking pictures at her direction, and almost certainly quizzed them intently about the workings of the art. As a Christmas present in 1863, when her husband was in Ceylon, her daughter and son-in-law gave her a camera, saying, "It may amuse you, Mother, to try to photograph during your solitude at Freshwater."[22] By the end of January 1864, Cameron was excited by her "first success." Virginia Woolf said, "All her sensibility was

expressed, and, what was perhaps more to the purpose, controlled in the new born art. The coal-house was turned into a dark room; the fowl-house was turned into a glass-house. Boatmen were turned into King Arthur; the village girls into Queen Guenevere. Tennyson was wrapped in rugs; Sir Henry Taylor was crowned with tinsel. The parlour-maid sat for her portrait and the guest had to answer the bell."[23] Julia Margaret Cameron refused to be bound by the photographic conventions of her day. In the words of Alvin Langdon Coburn, "Mrs. Cameron was an original woman; she never did things quite like other people."[24] She followed her own compass and produced, indeed embraced, photographs that were considered to be out of focus. Cameron turned to photography to seize the vivid images she imagined—the art allowed her to share with an audience her richly dramatic inner world.

Were Cameron's pictures out of focus? She did not seek out-of-focus images so much as accept them as a natural part of the working process. Only a novice—or a hidebound professional—would look at Cameron's photographs and perceive something imprecisely focused, sloppily produced, technically uninformed, or cavalier. Her son, himself a photographer, recalled that "when focusing and coming to something which to her eye was very beautiful, she stopped then, instead of screwing on the lens to the more definite focus, which all other photographers insist on."[25] Photographic materials in Cameron's day were sensitive only to light at the blue end of the spectrum, whereas the human eye is most responsive to those on nearly the opposite wavelengths in the yellow end. A simple lens would focus these varying wavelengths of light differently. Thus, when the lens was focused to make the image sharp to the eye, the wavelengths that the photographic materials would see were out of focus. To compensate for this, after composing and before taking the picture, the usual photographer would screw the lens in a little bit to accommodate the difference between the visual focus of the eye and the chemical focus of the plate. It was a technical demand known from the first days of photography, for both daguerreotypes and negatives. In contrast to most commercial photographers, Cameron did not give a whit for this convention. When the image looked beautiful to her, she took it, and happily accepted the slightly out-of-focus result on the collodion plate. Because of the spherical aberration of the lenses she used, this effect was especially pronounced on the peripheries of the image.

Cameron also eschewed the convention of locking her subject firmly in place, instead often embracing the blur of motion. Head rests and elbows propped on convenient tables were necessities in the earliest days of photography, when exposures could be measured in tens of minutes, and by the time exposures had dropped to seconds these practices had become orthodoxy. Unfortunately, this perceived need to freeze the subject led to frozen expressions. From a technical point of view, Cameron did everything wrong. She came in very close on her subject, which produced a life-size head but seriously limited her depth of field. She could have mitigated this with very bright studio lighting and stopping the lens down to a smaller aperture, but she wanted certain effects, and they often involved blocking some of the light, rather than augmenting it. With an unfettered subject framed very close and the lens open wide, conventional sharpness took a backseat to other aesthetic concerns.

In 1874, Cameron started writing her photographic memoirs, *Annals of My Glass House*, but the manuscript was never finished, and its fragments were not published until 1889. In 1875, she and her husband moved to Ceylon. Virginia Woolf wrote that "two coffins preceded them on board packed with glass and china, in case coffins should be unprocurable in the East ...."[26] Being much older, Charles was expected to die first, but Julia Margaret Cameron predeceased him in 1879 and is buried there. It was a shock to all who knew her. Lamented one well-informed critic, "So poor Julia Cameron is dead. She produced the finest photographs that I ever saw. She almost reconciled the artist to the lens ... she sought force and vigor, and got it ... she, herself was an ardent Ruskinite, and worshiped beauty with Hellenic fervor. With no grandeur of contour or feature herself, she would have no one about her, no tirewoman, no kitchen maid, who did not satisfy her aesthetic taste."[27]

Unlike many of the finest 19th century photographers, Julia Margaret Cameron never really dropped out of the history and never needed to be rediscovered. Perhaps through the efforts of her son H. H. Hay Cameron and somewhat through association with her many famous sitters, her photographs continued to enthrall audiences and challenge successive waves of new photographers. She was one of the few 19th century photographers that Alfred Stieglitz included in his modernist *Camera Work*, reproducing five of her portraits in photogravure. In 1915, Alvin Langdon Coburn gave her a central role in his *Exhibition of the Old Masters of Photography* in the Albright Art Gallery in Buffalo.[28] He observed, "Mrs. Cameron possessed perseverance, a love of human nature, and an irrepressible personality. She found in the camera an outlet for her creative energies exactly suited to her temperament."[29]

Virginia Woolf related the final story from Dimbula in Ceylon: "The birds were fluttering in and out of the open door; the photographs were tumbling over the tables; and, lying before a large open window, Mrs. Cameron saw the stars shining, breathed the one word 'Beautiful,' and so died."[30] At the start of her photographic journey, Julia Margaret Cameron said, "I longed to arrest all the beauty that came before me, and at length the longing was satisfied."[31]

[1] "Mrs. Cameron's Photographs," *Macmillan's Magazine*, v. 13 no. 77, January 1866, p. 230.

[2] Charles Hay Cameron, *Two Essays: On the Sublime and Beautiful, and on Duelling* (London: Ibotson and Palmer, 1835).

[3] Although Cameron photographed in London and elsewhere, she is most identified with Freshwater, in the Isle of Wight, where she lived and worked from 1860 to 1875. The difference in spelling between the family's coffee plantation, Dimbula in Ceylon (now Sri Lanka), and her Isle of Wight house has never been explained, and may have been a matter of phonetic spelling. The inscription establishes that this print was preserved by one of the children of Julia's sister Maria Mary "Mia" (1818–1892) and her husband Dr. John Jackson (1804–1887): Mary (m. Herbert William Fisher); Julia (m. Herbert Duckworth, then Sir Leslie Stephen); and Adeline (m. Henry Halford Vaughan, 1811–1895). The dating is based on a similar print in the National Media Museum, illustrated in Cox & Ford, fig. 22.

[4] Anne Thackeray Ritchie, "Reminiscences," in Anne Thackeray Ritchie and Henry Herschel Hay Cameron, *Alfred, Lord Tennyson and His Friends: A Series of 25 Portraits and Frontispiece in Photogravure from the Negatives of Mrs. Julia Margaret Cameron and H. H. H. Cameron* (London: T. Fisher Unwin, 1893), p. 9.

[5] Virginia Woolf, "Julia Margaret Cameron," in Roger Fry and Virginia Woolf, *Victorian Photographs of Famous Men & Fair Women* (London: The Hogarth Press, 1926); expanded and revised edition, Tristram Powell, editor (Boston: David R. Godine, 1973), p. 13.

[6] Alvin Langdon Coburn, "The Old Masters of Photography," *Century Magazine*, v. 90, October 1915, p. 916.

[7] Cox & Ford. A selection of other worthy books on her includes Colin Ford, *Julia Margaret Cameron: A Critical Biography* (Los Angeles: The J. Paul Getty Museum, 2003); Sylvia Wolf, *Julia Margaret Cameron's Women* (Chicago: Art Institute, 1998); Mike Weaver, *Julia Margaret Cameron 1815–1879* (Boston: Little, Brown, and Company, 1994); Colin Ford, *The Cameron Collection: An Album of Photographs by Julia Margaret Cameron Presented to Sir John Herschel* (Wokingham: Van Nostrand Reinhold, 1975); Helmut Gernsheim, *Julia Margaret Cameron: Her Life and Photographic Work* (London: The Fountain Press, 1948), revised edition (London: Gordon Fraser, 1975).

[8] Andrew Wynter, "Cartes de Visite," in *Curiosities of Toil and Other Papers* (London: Chapman and Hall, 1870), v. 1, pp. 133–134.

[9] They apologized, "We are sorry to have to speak thus severely on the works of a lady, but we feel compelled to do so in the interest of the art." *The Photographic Journal*, v. 9 no. 154, 15 February 1865, p. 196.

[10] "Mrs. Cameron's Photographs," *The Intellectual Observer; Review of Natural History, Microscopic Research, and Recreative Science*, v. 11 no. 1, February 1867, pp. 31–32.

[11] "The Late Mrs. Julia Hay Cameron," *The Times* (London), 4 March 1879, p. 10.

[12] See *Talbot Correspondence Project*, Docs. no. 07112 & 07114 (http://www.foxtalbot.dmu.ac.uk).

[13] Anne Thackeray Ritchie and Henry Herschel Hay Cameron, op. cit., p. 13.

[14] Her husband was Sir Josiah John Guest, 1st Baronet (1785–1853), owner of the Dowlais Iron Works in Glamorgan, a fellow Whig MP with W. H. F. Talbot in the Reform Parliament. In addition to becoming fabulously wealthy through his mining activities, Guest was a scientist. Sir David Brewster visited him in 1836, stopping off before continuing on to Lacock Abbey. See *Talbot Correspondence Project, Doc. no. 03361*. When Lady Charlotte's first husband died in 1853, she took over management of the Dowlais Iron Works, translating its technical documents into French and using her wealth in local philanthropy. In 1855, she married Charles Schreiber (1826–1884), a Cambridge scholar and MP, tutor to Kate's younger brother. She became an important collector of ceramics and antiques, contributing heavily to the Victoria and Albert Museum's ceramics collection, and to the fans and game boards collection now in the British Museum. Lady Charlotte is fondly remembered as an astute businesswoman, a discerning collector, a philanthropist and an English-born preserver of Welsh cultural heritage, all qualities that Cameron would have admired.

[15] Charlotte Guest, *The Mabinogion: from the Llyfr Coch o Hergest, and Other Ancient Welsh Manuscripts* (London: Longman, Orme, Brown, Green and Longmans, 1838). She worked from a collection of medieval manuscripts collectively known as the "Red Book of Hergest," in the archives of Jesus College, Oxford. They included pre-Christian Celtic mythology and other Iron Age stories and traditions.

[16] In fact, some of Tennyson's works were printed at the private press at Canford Manor, the seat of Lady Charlotte's son, Sir Ivor Bertie Guest (1835–1914). Charlotte, who had mastered copper plate engraving earlier, did some of the printing herself.

[17] Quoted from Revel Guest and Angela V. John, *Lady Charlotte: A Biography of the Nineteenth* Century (London: Weidenfeld and Nicolson, 1989), p. 146.

[18] Revel Guest and Angela V. John, op. cit., p. 162.

[19] Cameron wrote an enthusiastic and detailed letter to Alfred Lord Tennyson while a guest of Lady Charlotte's son. Quoted at length in Helmut Gernsheim, *Julia Margaret Cameron: Her Life and Photographic Work* (London: Gordon Fraser, 1975), pp. 21–22.

[20] Revel Guest and Angela V. John, op. cit., p. 201.

[21] ibid., pp. 243–244.

[22] See Joanne Lukitsh, "Before 1864: Julia Margaret Cameron's Early Work in Photography," in Cox & Ford, pp. 95–105.

[23] Virginia Woolf, "Julia Margaret Cameron," in Roger Fry and Virginia Woolf, op. cit., p. 18.

[24] Alvin Langdon Coburn, "The Old Masters of Photography," op. cit., p. 912.

[25] Quoted in Raymond Blathwayt, "How Celebrities Have Been Photographed," *The Windsor Magazine*, v. 2, December 1895, p. 648.

[26] Virginia Woolf, "Julia Margaret Cameron," in Roger Fry and Virginia Woolf, op. cit., p. 19.

[27] "Our London Correspondence," *The Liverpool Mercury*, 5 March 1879, p. 6.

[28] Alvin Langdon Coburn, "Preface," *Catalogue of an Exhibition of the Old Masters of Photography* (Buffalo, New York: The Buffalo Fine Arts Academy Albright Art Gallery, 1915).

[29] Alvin Langdon Coburn, "The Old Masters of Photography," op. cit., p. 912.

[30] Virginia Woolf, "Julia Margaret Cameron," in Roger Fry and Virginia Woolf, op. cit., p. 19.

[31] Anne Thackeray Ritchie and Henry Herschel Hay Cameron, op. cit., p. 11.

1. *Henry Halford Vaughan*
Albumen print from a wet collodion negative, copyrighted 30 June 1864. 20.0 x 17.5 cm oval mounted on 33.3 x 26.8 cm card. Provenance: Jackson-Vaughan family, by descent. Cox & Ford no. 824

In 1856, Henry Halford Vaughan (1811–1885), the Regius Professor of Modern History at Oxford, married Julia Margaret Cameron's niece Adeline Maria Jackson (1837–1881). Most of the items in this catalogue are from the personal collection assembled by this family.

Henry Halford Vaughan
Albumen print from a wet collodion negative, circa 1864–1870. 25.3 x 20.5 cm, arched top, mounted flush on card. Provenance: Jackson-Vaughan family, by descent. Cox & Ford no. 825

George Butler, the son of William Henry Fox Talbot's headmaster at Harrow, was spellbound by Vaughan, one of his professors at Oxford: "The lecture was a powerful, poetical, and sometimes sublime oration. Six hundred people were looking fixedly at him, holding their breath … Vaughan is almost too brilliant, both in conversation and in lecturing. He dazzles one."[1]

While his rhetorical wit dazzled his audiences both public and private, Vaughan projected a visual aura as well, one that Cameron captured and preserved in this startling portrait. "Vaughan's personal appearance was striking. His features were large, well-defined, and mobile, especially his eyes. They revealed at one time bright enjoyment of some humorous thought or word, or admiration of some strong and vigorous sentiment; at another time they were fixed on you with an intensity of expression that seem to pierce your very soul. He had an immense 'fell' of rough hair, of which his father the judge once said, 'To my certain knowledge the masons refused to buy Halford's hair to mix with their mortar; it was, they said, too coarse.' This gave a sort of wild Olympian character to his head."[2]

Another print of this image was inscribed by Cameron: "Hendon Lawn 1864 / Henry Halford Vaughan." Brent Lodge, Hendon, was the North London home of Cameron's sister Julia and Julia's husband, Dr. John Jackson.

[1] Josephine Elizabeth Grey Butler, *Recollections of George Butler* (Bristol: J. W. Arrowsmith, 1892), pp. 88–89.
[2] Henry L. Thompson, *Henry George Liddell, D.D., Dean of Christ Church, Oxford, A Memoir* (London: John Murray, 1899), pp. 124–125.

JULIA MARGARET CAMERON 13

2. Unknown photographer
"Mrs. Cameron, Charlie, & Henry"
Albumen print from a wet collodion negative, 1858.
21.0 x 15.9 cm, corners clipped, irregularly trimmed,
mounted on 55.5 x 40.5 cm board. Titled and dated in ink
on label on mount. Provenance: Lady Katherine Guest;
the Rubel Collection. Cox & Ford fig. 30

One is compelled to think that Cameron must have had an active role in the arrangement of this photograph, even to the point of it being a self-portrait, although her own photography was still five years distant.[3] Its structural simplicty mirrors that of her own portraits. Light and shadow form the dominant supporting elements here, subservient only to the arrangement of the sitters. It was taken in a simple, perhaps domestic, space, eschewing the elaborate trappings of a commercial photographer's studio. From a modern perspective, we might see a woman torn between her motherly duties and a cerebral life, though Cameron herself pointedly found these roles not at all contradictory, and, indeed, kept them in exquisite balance. In the picture, she carries on with her writing, gathering in her youngest son, Henry, while the more mature Charlie stands apart, foreshadowing the independence he would cultivate throughout life. Henry Herschel Hay Cameron (1852–1911) was named after Cameron's close friend Sir John Herschel. He flourished in London as a West End studio photographer before turning to an

ultimately unsuccessful career as an actor. Charles "Charlie" Hay Cameron (1849–1891), her third child and her first born in England, enjoyed a life of independent means and died in Germany. Neither ever married.

This photograph was extracted from an 1859 portrait album compiled by Lady Katharine "Kate" Gwladys Guest (1837–1926), the daughter of Cameron's London friend Lady Charlotte Elizabeth Guest, née Bertie (1812–1895).[4] Two of Kate's younger sisters were photographed by Cameron: Blanche Vere (1847–1919) and Mary Enid Evelyn (1844–1912). The latter married her cousin the explorer Austen Henry Layard (1817–1894), another Cameron subject. It seems probable that both Kate and her mother were photographed by Cameron as well, and perhaps someday they will be recognized among the unidentified portrait sitters.[5]

Two other prints of this image are known. One is in the National Portrait Gallery, London, and the other is in the Wilson Centre for Photography.[6]

[3] This is identified as being by an unknown photographer in Cox & Ford, p. 43. However, earlier sources all attributed it, perhaps echoing each other, often unreservedly, to Lewis Carroll, including: Mike Weaver, *Whisper of the Muse: The Overstone Album & Other Photographs by Julia Margaret Cameron* (Malibu: The J. Paul Getty Museum, 1986), p. 14; Violet Hamilton, *Annals of My Glass House: Photographs by Julia Margaret Cameron* (Seattle: University of Washington Press, 1996), p. 10. It is also possible that it was taken by one of Katherine Guest's brothers. Montague John Guest (1839–1909), a British Liberal politician later in life, was remembered as one "whose excellent photography was one among many of his varied artistic pursuits." He is looking through the viewfinder of a bellows folding camera in one portrait, but it has yet to be established when he started in the art. See Egan Mew's "Prefatory Note" to his posthumous *Lady Charlotte Schreiber's Journals* (London: John Lane, The Bodley Head, 1911), p. xxx.
[4] The album was inscribed "Kate Guest 1859," sold at Sotheby's Belgravia, 18 October 1974, lot 296, and subsequently broken up. In 1861, Kate changed her name when she married the Reverend Frederick Cecil Alderson (1836–1907), a chaplain to Queen Victoria and later canon of Peterborough.

[5] The Guests were frequent visitors to Little Holland House, the rural London home of Cameron's sister and the base of her intellectual life in London. However, in June 1859, unmarried Kate greatly alarmed her mother when she visited Little Holland House one evening on her own. In her diary, Lady Charlotte recorded that "I think these things wrong. While she remains under my roof I must be responsible and keep her with me, and prevent independent action. I know there cannot be a worse place to go alone than Little Holland House, amidst artists and musicians, and all the flattery and nonsense which is rife in that otherwise most agreeable society." Edited by The Earl of Bessborough, *Lady Charlotte Schreiber: Extracts from Her Journal 1853–1891* (London: John Murray, 1952), p. 107. Although mother and daughter did not speak for weeks afterwards, perhaps it was this visit that led to the present souvenir making its way into Kate's album. Ironically, at just about the time that Kate was assembling her album, Henry Talbot was negotiating with the Guest family firm, the Dowlais Iron Works, trying unsuccessfully to extract the mineral wealth in his Wiltshire lands. See *Talbot Correspondence Project, Doc. no. 09289 and passim* (http// www.foxtalbot.dmu.ac.uk).
[6] These prints are untrimmed, showing the edges of the collodion negative, and carry no inscription.

Mrs Cameron, Charlie, & Henry. 1858.

3. *"My printing of ferns"*
Photogram on albumen paper, likely earlier than 1863.
19.3 x 14.9 cm. Titled in ink on verso. Provenance:
Thackery & Robertson Gallery. Cox & Ford fig. 76

Making photograms—photographs made without a camera by arranging objects on light-sensitive paper—was a logical first step for many photographers. For early inventors such as Thomas Wedgwood or William Henry Fox Talbot, they facilitated the process of experiment and discovery. For later amateurs, they provided a seemingly simple introduction to the art. Photograms, or sun drawings, were popular as parlor entertainment, particularly for women, because they fit neatly into the format of scrapbooks and keepsakes.[7] Sometimes they were used for serious and sustained study, as in the case of the cyanotyped algae of Anna Atkins.[8]

No hint has been found in Cameron's writings as to when she took up the practice of photograms. Since this negative is on albumen paper, it would have been made in 1852 or later. Was it an early probing of the possibilities of the medium, done sometime in the years leading up to what Cameron called her "first success" with the camera, at the start of 1864? Was it a step in learning how to print her glass negatives, or maybe a creation made in parallel with her photography, meant to stand on its own merits?[9] No other example of Cameron's photogram work is known to have survived.[10]

According to Alvin Langdon Coburn, "Printing-frames, I have been told, were on fine days always to be seen at Dimbola, and the stains of nitrate of silver bedecked most of the table linen of the establishment; but Mrs. Cameron got her results."[11]

[7] The work of the young Bessie Rayner Parkes is a good example. See *Sun Pictures Catalogue Ten: British Paper Negatives 1839–1864* (New York: Hans P. Kraus, Jr., Inc., 2001), pp. 36–40.
[8] See Larry J. Schaaf, *Sun Gardens: Victorian Photographs by Anna Atkins* (New York: Aperture, 1985).
[9] This negative is dated "about 1862" in Cox & Ford, fig. 76, p. 103.
[10] There is a hybrid Cameron photographic portrait of Mary Ryan, printed with a surround of photogram flowers, illustrated in Joanne Lukitsh, *Julia Margaret Cameron* (London: Phaidon, 2006), pl. 2.
[11] Alvin Langdon Coburn, "The Old Masters of Photography," *Century Magazine*, v. 90, October 1915, p. 916.

4. *Sir Henry Taylor*
Albumen print from a wet collodion negative, 1865.
25.4 x 21.7 cm visible area in oval window with gilt bevel,
mounted on 30.0 x 27.5 cm card. Provenance: Jackson-
Vaughan family, by descent. Cox & Ford no. 781

According to Adolphus Liddell, onetime neighbor of Cameron and a relative of Alice Liddell: "Sir Henry Taylor, the poet, wore a cape and a wide-awake, an uncommon get-up in those pre-æsthetic days … he was a tall man, although he had rather a stoop, with a very fine head and a long grey beard, and a somewhat languid dreamy expression."[12] He might just as well have been describing this Rembrandtish portrait by Cameron, which captures Taylor perfectly.

"Sir Henry Taylor, whose fine old face appears again and again in Mrs. Cameron's gallery, was ever at her beck and call. Indeed he was her devoted slave, and weekly he would sit to her as a model for some of her idyllic subjects. Sometimes on going into the little studio chicken-house one would find him as a king, with a poker in his hand in lieu of a scepter; on another occasion he would play 'Friar Laurence' to some village maiden's 'Juliet;' he would be 'Merlin' to a dainty 'Vivien,' or as 'Prospero' he would sit and talk with 'Miranda.' "[13] Virginia Woolf quoted Taylor in reflecting, "that though Julia Cameron and her sisters 'have more of hope than of reason,' still 'the humanities are stronger in them than the sentimentalities,' and they generally brought their eccentric undertakings to a successful end."[14]

The distinguished poet and author facing Cameron had a most unpromising start. Henry Taylor (1800–1886) was the son of a widowed gentleman farmer and amateur classicist who ran an intellectual but melancholy household. Henry was a great disappointment as a child, the least promising of three brothers, and he went to sea at the age of fourteen. He returned four years later, living briefly with his two brothers in London until they succumbed to typhus, then returned to his father's grim household with its rich library. He eventually moved back to London to start a literary career, and unlike most developing writers, the job he took to support himself, in the civil service, turned into a lucrative career.

Taylor was most proud of his poetry but is remembered in some circles primarily for writings that documented a period of British diplomatic history. He spent nearly five decades as the senior clerk for the Caribbean Colonies in the Colonial Office. His long and distinguished service there, which included overseeing the elimination of slavery in the West Indies, brought him into contact with many leading political figures. The depiction of Taylor in Cameron's portrait would seem at odds with the image of a senior civil servant. His spectacular beard was the result of an 1859 illness, which left him unable to shave, and this visual pendant had been growing for six years before Cameron photographed him.

Taylor said to his friend Mrs. Cameron, "As of your photographs, so of my poems. If people will only admire enthusiastically, you will give profusely, and of course enthusiastic admirers increase and multiply. For my own part, I think enthusiasm should pay its own way, and I would send enthusiasts to their booksellers. Their enthusiasm would cool down a little."[15]

[12] A "wide-awake" was a low-crowned, very wide-brimmed hat. Adolphus George Charles Liddell, *Notes from the Life of an Ordinary Mortal: Being a Record of Things Done, Seen, and Heard, at School, College, and in the World during the Latter Half of the 19th Century* (London: John Murray, 1911), pp. 4–5.
[13] Raymond Blathwayt, "How Celebrities Have Been Photographed," *The Windsor Magazine*, v. 2, December 1895, p. 640.
[14] Virginia Woolf, "Julia Margaret Cameron," in Roger Fry and Virginia Woolf, *Victorian Photographs of Famous Men & Fair Women* (London: The Hogarth Press, 1926); expanded and revised edition, Tristram Powell, editor (Boston: David R. Godine, 1973), p. 17.
[15] Quoted by Alvin Langdon Coburn, "The Old Masters of Photography," *Century Magazine*, v. 90, October 1915, p. 914.

5. *The Communion*[16]
Albumen print from a wet collodion negative, 1865–1866.
34.3 x 27.2 cm mounted flush on card. Provenance:
Jackson-Vaughan family, by descent. Cox & Ford no. 106

This is a fine example of Cameron's "Milkmaid Madonnas", ordinary salt-of-the-earth people temporarily placed on a stage by Cameron. Phyllis Rose felt that "Cameron's response to beauty, eradicating class as it did, was so extreme as to constitute an almost political statement."[17] But Cameron's statement was simply that beauty was beautiful no matter the source, and that roles in life and roles in art were entirely separate.

In this picture, Cameron has very cleverly focused on the near flowers in the upper and lower areas of the image, keeping our eyes from staring too intently at the subjects, and thus coaxing them gently into our imagination.

The sitters here were local to Freshwater. Mary Ann Hillier (1847–1936), the daughter of the town shoemaker, served as a parlor maid in Cameron's household from 1861–1875. Cameron probably met her through Mary's older sister Sophia, who was a maid in the Tennyson household. After Cameron moved to Ceylon, Mary Ann married and stayed in Freshwater for the rest of her life. The girl was Elizabeth Louisa "Topsy" Keown (1859–1952), the daughter of Thomas Keown, a master gunner in the coastal brigade at Freshwater. She eventually married an army schoolmaster and moved to India.

[16] The title is from Julian Cox, *In Focus: Julia Margaret Cameron* (Los Angeles: The J. Paul Getty Museum, 1996), p. 84.
[17] An evocative term first used to review a Grünewald opera in "The Artist's Life," *The Times* (London), 24 June 1939, p. 10. It was applied to Cameron in Phyllis Rose, "Milkmaid Madonnas: An Appreciation of Cameron's Portraits of Women," in Sylvia Wolf, *Julia Margaret Cameron's Women* (New Haven: Yale University Press, 1998), pp. 12–21.

JULIA MARGARET CAMERON

6. *"Baby Blossom"*
Albumen print from a wet collodion negative, circa 1866.
34.1 x 27.8 cm mounted on 52.3 x 45.4 cm card. Signed,
inscribed in ink "From life not enlarged," and titled in
pencil, with Colnaghi blindstamp on mount.
Provenance: Hansen Collection. Cox & Ford no. 878

This almost larger-than-life head was well known to
Cameron. It belonged to Alice Jessie Keown, who was born
in Freshwater on 25 April 1861, the third daughter of
Thomas Keown (see p. 20). In 1892, she married Henry
Percival Johnson. Cameron also photographed Alice's older
sister Elizabeth and her younger brother Percy. Alice herself
was never known as Baby Blossom, so perhaps Cameron
took her inspiration from Ida White's recently published
poem:

My own dear baby-blossom! none more fair
E'er claimed from woman's love a mother's care.
When first I pressed thee to my throbbing breast,
And hushed thy infant murmurings into rest,
Wild throes of rapturous joy my being moved—
Was ever flow'ret yet more fondly loved?[18]

—Ida White, 1865

No other print of this image is known.

[18] Ida White, "Violet, Victoria," in *Lady Blanche and Other Poems* (London: Hamilton, Adams, & Co., 1875), p. 99. In spite of the apparent sentimentality of this poem, its author was a force to be reckoned with: "Her later life has been a stormy one, and she appears to be an Anarchist and Freethinker." David J. O'Donoghue, *The Poets of Ireland: A Biographical Dictionary with Bibliographical Particulars* (London: Printed by Paternoster Steam Press, 1892), p. 257.

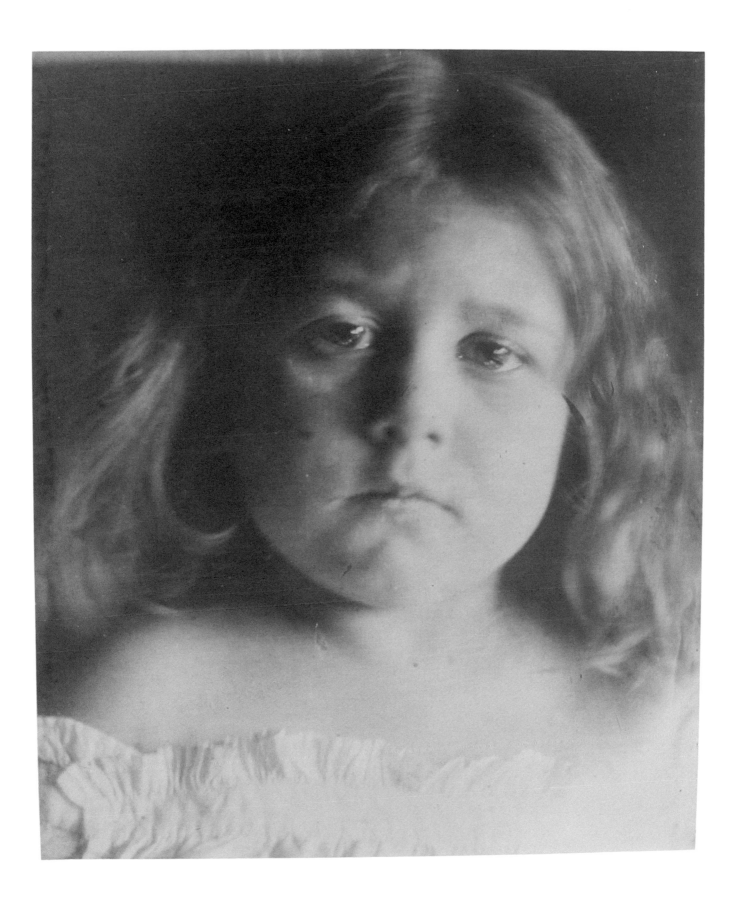

JULIA MARGARET CAMERON

7. *Madonna and Child*
Albumen print from a wet collodion negative, June 1866.
35.4 x 28.7 cm mounted on 53.6 x 44.5 cm card, ruled
in gilt. Signed and inscribed in ink "From Life," with
Colnaghi blindstamp on mount. Inscribed in a later hand
in ink "Whitfield / Allensmore / Hereford" on mount
verso. Provenance: P & D Colnaghi; Clive family, by
descent. Variant of Cox & Ford no. 136

Anne Thackeray Ritchie testified that "Mrs. Cameron's
power was a peculiar one; many people can feel beauty and
record it; she had an intuition, not only for appreciating, but
for creating, with the materials at hand, something which
was her own, and which she gave to us. She had a directness
and originality which was all her own, which she applied to
other things than chemicals; she made every day in the week
a Saint's day, every commonplace event into something
special, just as she transformed a village maiden into a
Madonna, or a country bumpkin into a Paladin."[19]

This is another of Cameron's "Milkmaid Madonnas",[20]
photographs in which commoners were temporarily ele-
vated to a status they would never know in their everyday
life. This Madonna is Mary Ann Hillier, Cameron's parlor
maid (see item no. 5, p. 20). Percy Seymour Keown
(1864–1901) was also local talent, the son of Thomas Keown
(see p. 20). His sisters Elizabeth and Alice also sat for Cameron. He eventually became a seaman.

[19] Anne Thackeray Ritchie and Henry Herschel Hay Cameron, *Alfred, Lord Tennyson and His Friends: A Series of 25 Portraits and Frontispiece in Photogravure from the Negatives of Mrs. Julia Margaret Cameron and H.H.H. Cameron* (London: T. Fisher Unwin, 1893), p. 12.
[20] An evocative term first used to review a Grünewald opera in "The Artist's Life," *The Times* (London), 24 June 1939, p. 10. It was applied to Cameron in Phyllis Rose, "Milkmaid Madonnas: An Appreciation of Cameron's Portraits of Women," in Sylvia Wolf, *Julia Margaret Cameron's Women* (New Haven: Yale University Press, 1998), pp. 12–21.

JULIA MARGARET CAMERON

8. *"Mary Mother"*
Albumen print from a wet collodion negative, April 1867.
33.9 x 26.6 cm mounted on 51.1 x 44.3 cm card, ruled in
gilt. Signed, titled, and inscribed in ink "From life / Fresh-
Water / copy right registered photograph / Given with
Mrs. Cameron's best love," with Colnaghi blindstamp on
mount. Provenance: Jackson-Vaughan family, by descent.
Cox & Ford no. 101

In this extraordinary, beautiful, and peaceful portrait, Cameron has carefully lit her subject from the side and rear, creating a profile framed by a circle of dark cloth. The seemingly misplaced focus on the distant eye actually draws us across the entire face and into the picture, whereas the more conventional approach of focusing on the near eye would have arrested us there. The model is not one of Cameron's famous social acquaintances. One contemporary critic observed that Cameron was "evidently endowed with an unusual amount of artistic tact; she knows a beautiful head when she sees it—a very rare facility; and her position in literary and aristocratic society gives her the pick of the most beautiful and intellectual heads in the world. Other photographers have had to take such subjects as they could get. With few exceptions, all Mrs. Cameron's subjects are of a very high order of beauty. But intellect and beauty have apparently not been the only qualities considered in her choice. She has carefully selected the beauty which depends on form."[21]

The lovely woman here was Cameron's parlor maid, Mary Ann Hillier (see item no. 5, p. 20).

[21] "Mrs. Cameron's Photographs," *Macmillan's Magazine*, v. 13 no. 77, January 1866, p. 230.

From life April 1867 Fresh Water copy right registered Photograph Julia Margaret Cameron

Mary Mother

JULIA MARGARET CAMERON

9. *Sir John Herschel*
Albumen print from a wet collodion negative, 4–7 April 1867. 35.5 x 25.5 cm on 36.6 x 27.6 cm paper, untrimmed, mounted on 40.0 x 30.3 cm card. Provenance: Jackson-Vaughan family, by descent. Cox & Ford no. 674

Cameron received some of her strongest support from what might seem like the most unlikely of allies. Sir John Frederick William Herschel (1792–1871), one of a distinguished dynasty of astronomers in the 18th and 19th centuries, was an exacting scientist. His knowledge of all aspects of the universe, celestial and terrestrial, is intimidating even to the modern mind.[22] An accomplished draughtsman, his detailed research was the technical underpinning of much early photography. Precision in thought and expression were essential to him. In spite of this, nobody better understood what Julia Margaret Cameron was trying to achieve in her photographs. Herschel immediately comprehended that Cameron's unorthodox attitude toward focus and her acceptance of technical anomalies in her negatives and prints were subservient to the beauty that she sought.

It was Herschel who first introduced the idea of photography to Cameron in its earliest years when she was in India, long before she took up the camera herself. In sending him some prints, Cameron admiringly wrote, "your eye can best detect & your imagination conceive all that is to be done & is still left undone. For you were my first Teacher & to you I owe all the first experiences & insights which were given to me when you sent me in India a score of years ago … the first specimens of Talbotype, of photographs coloured by the juices of plants &c &c."[23]

This is one of the iconic portraits of Herschel taken by Cameron, and it is safe to say that most people today think of this visage when they think of him. Herschel was in fact a very dashing and vital man when photography was being invented.[24] At the time of this picture almost three decades later, still full of force and dignity, he was nearing the end of his life. Herschel had sacrificed his health in service to his country, reluctantly accepting the post of master of the Mint (following in the footsteps of Sir Isaac Newton) to bring scientific order to Britain's currency in the run-up to the Crimean War. The pressures of constant meetings and the insalubrious atmosphere of urban London took their toll, softened only by the frequent use of laudanum. In 1867, on his 75th birthday, the normally optimistic Herschel observed, "Comparing my state of health & vigour with what it was this day 12 month ago it seems impossible that I should ever see another birthday."[25] He was to live another four years, but

it was in this greatly diminished state of physical health that he received Cameron less than a month later. "With a little cart and photographic apparatus all complete," Cameron "suddenly arrived, gipsy fashion, at the gate one day, and took the old gentleman just as he was."[26]

Although this portrait was widely admired and often printed, this particular print is perhaps unique in being untrimmed, showing the periphery of the negative and the evidence of Cameron's coating techniques. Herschel recorded in his diary on 4 April 1867, "Mrs Cameron came with her maid Mary Ryan and an immense Van load of Photographic apparatus. Camera Baths Glasses Sensitizing apparatus Developing apparatus & Chemicals!!!" The next two days were given over to "energetic" and "intense" photography. Finally, on 8 April, "Mrs Cameron & 'Mary Ryan' left full of Photographs and with hands as black as coals."[27]

This print was perhaps one of the last to be made from this negative. Two years after she captured Herschel's face, a distressed Cameron took the negative to a meeting of the Photographic Society of London. It had developed a network of fine cracks (visible in the area of the nose and elsewhere). The opinion of the experts was that the collodion and the varnish she put over it expanded and contracted at different rates, disrupting the gossamer image.[28]

[22] A part of this range is demonstrated in his youthful *Preliminary Discourse on the Study of Natural Philosophy* (London: Longman, Rees, Ormé, Brown, & Green, 1830).
[23] Letter, Cameron to Herschel, 31 December 1864. Reproduced in facsimile in Colin Ford, *The Cameron Collection: An Album of Photographs by Julia Margaret Cameron Presented to Sir John Herschel* (London: National Portrait Gallery, 1975), pp. 140–141.
[24] See the miniature portrait made of him in 1829 and the 1843 Jensen oil that Maggie Herschel considered to be especially truthful in Larry J. Schaaf, *Out of the Shadows: Herschel, Talbot & the Invention of Photography* (London: Yale University Press, 1992), figs. 8 and 44.
[25] Entry for 7 March 1867. WO47, Herschel Collection, Harry Ransom Humanities Research Center, The University of Texas at Austin.
[26] Quoted from H.H. Hay Cameron in Raymond Blathwayt, "How Celebrities Have Been Photographed," *The Windsor Magazine*, v. 2, December 1895, p. 643.
[27] Herschel, 1867 *Diary*. WO47, Herschel Collection, Harry Ransom Humanities Research Center, The University of Texas at Austin.
[28] "Photographic Society of London, Meeting of 11 May 1869," *The Journal of the Photographic Society*, 15 May 1869, pp. 33–34.

JULIA MARGARET CAMERON

10. *Thomas Carlyle*
Albumen print from a wet collodion negative, copyrighted
8 June 1867. 31.7 x 25.3 cm mounted on 46.5 x 35.9 cm
card, ruled in gilt. Signed, titled "Carlyle," and inscribed
in ink "From life Registered Photograph" on mount.
Provenance: Jackson-Vaughan family, by descent.
Cox & Ford no. 629

On entering the parlor of Amos Bronson Alcott, the American intellectual and friend of Ralph Waldo Emerson,
Alexander Ireland observed that amongst the "quaint mottos
and pictures hung on the walls, the most noticeable picture
is a photograph of Carlyle. It is what is called a 'Cameron
photograph.' An English woman of rank takes these photographs of distinguished men just for her own amusement.
The camera is set out of focus, the heads nearly life-size, and
the general effect is singular—interesting, if nothing else. All
you can see against a black background is the indistinct out-
lines of a shaggy white head and beard and sharp features.
With all deference to Mr. Carlyle, we must say that he looks
like an old beggar."[29]

It is impossible to see this image of the Scottish social
commentator for the first time without being arrested by its
rough-hewn severity. The slight blur of Carlyle's moving
head heightens the effect, while the horizontal lines in the
collodion coating do nothing to diminish it. Cameron's
frontal variant of this portrait caused Colin Ford to exclaim:
"Carlyle like a rough block of Michelangelo's sculpture."[30] It
is a wholly appropriate image for an irascible writer whose
caustic pen brought an almost savage realism to historical
writing.

Carlyle wrote to Cameron that "I work all day and all days,
riding abroad a little in the dark like a distracted ghost, trying if I can keep alive till the thing gets done, and gloomily
returning to my den again."[31] After a long association, she
sought him for a sitting, but he never fit her into his sched-
ule. But "on another occasion when in London, Thomas
Carlyle rode slowly by Mrs. Cameron's house. She caught
sight of him, but he did not hear her voice. A boy ran after

him, and instead of being irritated he tipped him, returned
to Mrs. Cameron with the most courtly of bows, and then
and there was taken the photograph."[32]

Reviewing H. H. Hay Cameron's 1893 book on Tennyson's friends, *The Nation* marveled at "the magnificent
profile of Carlyle … it is the most remarkable thing in the
book, and one of the best portraits in existence. Only the
great masters of portraiture have done anything at once so
fine in aspect and so convincing in representation of character, and it reminds one rather of Velasquez or Rembrandt
than of ordinary photography."[33] On receiving this portrait,
Carlyle himself wrote to Cameron in his characteristic style:
"Has something of likeness, though terrifically ugly and
woebegone! My candid opinion. T. Carlyle."[34]

[29] Alexander Ireland, *Ralph Waldo Emerson: His Life, Genius, and Writings,
a Biographical Sketch*, 2nd edition, largely augmented (London: Simpkin,
Marshall, & Co., 1882), pp. 275–276.
[30] Colin Ford, *The Cameron Collection: An Album of Photographs by Julia
Margaret Cameron Presented to Sir John Herschel* (London: National Portrait
Gallery, 1975), p. 117.
[31] "Chronicle and Comment," *The Bookman: A Literary Journal*, v. 6 no. 4,
December 1897, p. 279.
[32] Raymond Blathwayt, "How Celebrities Have Been Photographed,"
The Windsor Magazine, v. 2, December 1895, p. 643.
[33] *The Nation*, v. 57 no. 1480, 9 November 1893, p. 356. The review was of
Anne Thackeray Ritchie, *Alfred, Lord Tennyson and His Friends: A Series of
25 Portraits and Frontispiece in Photogravure from the Negatives of Mrs. Julia
Margaret Cameron and H. H. H. Cameron* (London: T. Fisher Unwin, 1893).
The reviewer felt that most readers would remember the engraving done
by Timothy Cole, after Cameron's photograph, published as the frontis to
Scribner's Monthly, v. 22 no. 1, May 1881.
[34] "Chronicle and Comment," *The Bookman: A Literary Journal*, v. 6 no. 4,
December 1897, p. 280.

11. *The Echo*
Albumen print from a wet collodion negative, September 1868. 31.5 x 23.9 cm mounted on 58.1 x 46.3 cm card, ruled in gilt. Signed, captioned "Hatty Campbell," and inscribed in ink "From life / For dear Halford," with Colnaghi blindstamp on mount. Provenance: Jackson-Vaughan family, by descent. Cox & Ford no. 183

The beautiful and musical mountain nymph named after Ekho, the Greek word for sound, prized too highly the resonance of her own voice. No matter which version of the myth one follows, she meets with a cruel end. In the most familiar version, Zeus's wife Hera felt betrayed by Echo and condemned her to repeat the sounds that others made. In another telling, Echo refused the advances of Pan, who then had her killed and her remains scattered over the earth, where they continued to repeat the last words of others.

Yet Cameron's portrait seems to totally deny a voice—her subject has an almost deliberately closed mouth. It seems more likely that the allusion was to Christina Rosetti's 1854 poem, "The Echo," about communicating with a lost lover through dreams:

> Come to me in the silence of the night;
>   Come in the speaking silence of a dream;
> Come with soft rounded cheeks and eyes as bright
>   As sunlight on a stream;
> Come back in tears,
>   O memory, hope, love of finished years.

One is slightly aware of the careless folds in the temporary backdrop set up by Cameron, but, more than anything, this photograph is a clear depiction of a particular person. Cameron identified her sitter as Hatty Campbell, whose identity long remained a mystery, with only the speculation that she was a visitor to the Isle of Wight. Emily Tennyson praised the "the wonderful photographs of the Miss Campbells" that Cameron showed her.[35] Cameron is known to have done six photographs of Hatty, one of the somewhat older Eleanor Campbell, and two with the sisters posed together.[36] This is the only positively dated one, and the others appear to be from the same time, supporting the idea that these were taken during a visit.

Although the identity of the sisters has been elusive in the past, they can almost certainly be identified now as the daughters of Major General John Francis Glencairn Campbell (1810–1870), a Scottish-born leader of the 91st Argyllshire Highlanders, and his wife, the Canadian-born Katherine Elizabeth, née Alexander (b. 1820), the daughter of a captain in the Royal Engineers. They married in St. Helena in 1836 while he was on duty, and their numerous children were born in various stations thereafter. Eleanor (or Ellinor) Jane Campbell was born in 1842 at Fort Peddie at the Cape of Good Hope. The Camerons were living in India by then, but it is quite possible that the families were acquainted through mutual friends. Four years later, John Francis distinguished himself in the 7th Kaffir War and by 1848 was transferred back to England. In 1851, his regiment was sent to Ireland, and in 1852 Eugenia (sometimes Eugenie) Francis Harriet Campbell was born in Dublin. Hatty is a common nickname for Harriet, and might well have been used instead of Eugenia. Little is known about Eleanor; she was living with an aunt and uncle in Sussex in 1861 and just might be the spinster who died there in 1891. Eugenia was living with her widowed mother in the Channel Islands by 1871, and died in a nursing home in Hampshire in 1939. Remaining unmarried, was she the faithful keeper of the lost love in Rosetti's poem? In Cameron's moving portrait, she will always be sixteen.

[35] Cox & Ford, p. 512.
[36] Illustrated in Cox & Ford, nos. 180–188.

Duffy Campbell.

JULIA MARGARET CAMERON

12. *"Hypatia, Marie Spartali"*
Albumen print from a wet collodion negative, 1867 or
1868. 31.9 x 24.8 cm mounted on 42.5 x 31.9 cm card,
ruled in gilt. Signed, titled, and inscribed in ink "From
life" on mount. Provenance: Jackson-Vaughan family,
by descent. Cox & Ford no. 469

The model here presents a very different appearance from many of Cameron's other milkmaids and daughters of friends, perhaps because she herself was an artists' model and an accomplished watercolorist. Marie Euphrosyne Spartali (1843–1927) was the daughter of the Greek consul in London. A pupil of the Pre-Raphaelite painter Ford Madox Brown, she first exhibited at the Dudley Gallery, and in 1867, about the time of this photograph, she was admitted into the Royal Academy. Spartali married the American painter and photographer William James Stillman (1828–1901) in 1871.[37] Before posing for Cameron, she had modeled for Dante Gabriel Rossetti, Ford Madox Brown, and Edward Burne-Jones.

Hypatia of Alexandria was a Greek scholar and the country's first mathematician, known as much for her beauty as for her oratory. She was brutally murdered by Christian zealots. Her story was brought back to life by Charles Kingsley's novel *Hypatia: Or New Foes with an Old Face*, published in *Fraser's Magazine* in 1851–1852, in which she was "also known as the 'Divine Pagan,' her combination of wisdom and beauty, as well as her martyrdom, stirred the sympathy of Victorian readers."[38]

It is possible that Cameron took her inspiration for this image from another source. Sir John Herschel's close Scottish friend Mary Somerville (1780–1872) was a brilliant writer on mathematics, at times suffering in a male-dominated society. She was the Victorian Hypatia.[39]

In April 1868, Cameron wrote excitedly to her patron Sir Henry Cole of the South Kensington Museum (now the Victoria and Albert), "Mr. Spartali was a most glowing & enthusiastic admirer of my works with a very grateful note of thanks he gave me an order for 40 copies of his daughter's pictures enclosing a cheque for 20 guineas."[40] As strong and as popular as this image was, the print sellers' price increase from £1 to £2 was justified by the explanation, "as the glass is now injured & perfect copies are scarce."[41]

[37] See Andrew Szegedy-Maszak, "An American on the Acropolis: William James Stillman," in *Antiquity & Photography: Early Views of Ancient Mediterranean Sites* (Los Angeles: The J. Paul Getty Museum, 2005), pp. 148–195.
[38] Sylvia Wolf, *Julia Margaret Cameron's Women* (New Haven: Yale University Press, 1998), p. 230.
[39] This connection was first made in "Illustrious Women of Our Time: Mrs. Somerville," *The Lady's Newspaper*, 21 February 1852, p. 99.
[40] A guinea was 21 shillings, or £1 plus one shilling, and was the traditional way of settling gentlemen's debts. Letter, Cameron to Cole, 7 April 1868. Archives, Victoria and Albert Museum.
[41] Cox & Ford, p. 261.

from life   Julia Margaret Cameron

Hypatia

JULIA MARGARET CAMERON   35

13. *Charles Darwin*
Albumen print from a wet collodion negative,
16 July–21 August 1868. 30.3 x 25.0 cm mounted on
58.4 x 46.4 cm card, ruled in gilt. Signed, inscribed "From
life," and autographed "Ch. Darwin" in ink, with Colnaghi
blindstamp on mount. Provenance: Jackson-Vaughan
family, by descent. Variant of Cox & Ford no. 645

Looking at Cameron's portraits, Anne Ritchie Thackeray observed: "The sun paints the shadow of life, and the human instinct and intelligence bestowed upon this shadow create in it that essence of life and light which is so priceless in a picture."[42] The present image is one of only two known copies of this particular Cameron portrait of Charles Robert Darwin (1809–1882), the famous and controversial naturalist. It is not represented in Cox & Ford, where three other versions, all apparently taken during the same session as this one, are shown.[43] Helmut Gernsheim had the other copy in the 1940s, but its present location is unknown.[44]

In the summer of 1868, Darwin was actively writing *The Descent of Man*, when illness forced him to take a break, and he journeyed to Freshwater, the Isle of Wight. He was there from 16 July until 21 August. Darwin's son remembered that Cameron "received the whole family with open-hearted kindness and hospitality, and my father always retained a warm feeling of friendship for her. She made an excellent photograph of him, which was published with the inscription written by him: 'I like this photograph very much better than any other which has been taken of me.' "[45]

Darwin's friend and the director of Kew Gardens, Joseph Dalton Hooker, visited Darwin at Freshwater and was photographed by Cameron. She must have printed her precious Darwin negatives immediately, for just before leaving Freshwater, he wrote to Hooker: "How about photographs? Can you spare time for a line to our dear Mrs. Cameron? She came to see us off, and loaded us with presents of photographs, and Erasmus called after her, 'Mrs. Cameron, there are six people in this house all in love with you.' When I paid her, she cried out, 'Oh what a lot of money!' and ran to boast to her husband."[46]

Alvin Langdon Coburn related that, upon receiving a copy of the naturalist's portrait from Cameron, "The great Darwin wrote to her … 'there are sixteen people in my house, and all your friends.' We can well understand this when we see the result she achieved … what a head it was! One cannot help envying Mrs. Cameron her opportunity."[47]

[42] Anne Thackeray Ritchie and Henry Herschel Hay Cameron, *Alfred, Lord Tennyson and His Friends: A Series of 25 Portraits and Frontispiece in Photogravure from the Negatives of Mrs. Julia Margaret Cameron and H. H. H. Cameron* (London: T. Fisher Unwin, 1893), p. 11.
[43] Cox & Ford nos. 644–646 were the Darwin portraits identified at the time.
[44] Gernsheim illustrated it as part of the "Author's Collection" in *Julia Margaret Cameron: Her Life and Photographic Work* (London: The Fountain Press, 1948), plate 5 and repeated in the revised edition (London: Gordon Fraser, 1975), plate 124. This portrait of Darwin was not included in Gernsheim's collection when he sold it to the Harry Ransom Humanities Research Center of The University of Texas at Austin in 1963 and it has not been traced elsewhere.
[45] Francis Darwin, *The Life and Letters of Charles Darwin, Including an Autobiographical Chapter* (London: John Murray, 1887), v. 3, p. 92.
[46] Letter of 23 August 1868, quoted in Francis Darwin, op. cit., v. 3, pp. 101–102.
[47] Alvin Langdon Coburn, "The Old Masters of Photography," *Century Magazine*, v. 90, October 1915, p. 915.

from life   Julia Margaret Cameron

Ch. Darwin

14. *Henry Wadsworth Longfellow*
Albumen print from a wet collodion negative, copyrighted
23 July 1868. 35.5 x 26.3 cm mounted on 58.2 x 46.4 cm
card, ruled in gilt. Signed, dated, autographed "Henry W.
Longfellow," and inscribed in ink "From Life registered
photograph / Thirty shillings having genuine written auto-
graph," with Colnaghi blindstamp on mount. Provenance:
Jackson-Vaughan family, by descent. Cox & Ford no. 712

The great American poet Henry Wadsworth Longfellow
(1807–1882) took several European tours in connection with
professorships of modern language. He had met Tennyson in
Boston, so it was natural that he should be drawn into
Cameron's web when he visited England.

   This photograph was taken at Freshwater, where "Tennyson was constantly in the studio. One morning Mrs. Cameron was seated at breakfast when there came to her her
friend and nurse with the information that 'Mr. Tennyson
and a strange gentleman were at the door and wanted to
speak to her.' She hurried out to find Tennyson and Longfellow awaiting her coming. 'I have brought you a great man,
who will let you immortalise him,' growled the poet. 'This
is Longfellow; you know him by name, now you know him
in the flesh. I will leave you now. Longfellow, you'll have to
do whatever she tells you. I'll come back soon and see what
is left of you.' "[48]

[48] Raymond Blathwayt, "How Celebrities Have Been Photographed,"
The Windsor Magazine, v. 2, December 1895, p. 639.

From life. Registered Photograph July 1868   Julia Margaret Cameron.

Henry W. Longfellow.

JULIA MARGARET CAMERON

15. *Herr Joseph Joachim*
Albumen print from a wet collodion negative, copyrighted
3 April 1868. 31.6 x 26.4 cm mounted on 58.4 x 46.4 cm
card, ruled in gilt. Signed, titled "Herr Joachim," and
inscribed in ink "From life / For dear Halford Vaughan,"
with Colnaghi blindstamp on mount. Provenance: Jackson-
Vaughan family, by descent. Cox & Ford no. 695

The Hungarian musician Joseph Joachim (1831–1907), the
leader of Franz Liszt's orchestra in Leipzig, regularly toured
throughout Europe. In 1868, Joachim had returned to London for the annual and hugely fashionable Monday Popular
Concerts, held before consistently large and enthusiastic
audiences in St. James's Hall. The season had started in February, and his last performance before returning to Germany
was on 28 March, which was right around the time this
picture was taken. Joachim played Beethoven, "the prince
of composers and the prince of violinists" in "irresistible"
performances, done by "a great executant, he is a great
artist, who sets about his work lovingly, and with a reverence
for it."[49]

Another print from this negative was inscribed by
Cameron: "Herr Joachim taken at South Kensington
Museum 1868." It was fitting and perhaps natural that this
portrait was taken in the building that is now the Victoria
and Albert Museum. Joachim's research on musical instruments was as "remarkable as his powers of display,"[50] and
from its beginnings, the museum collected the musical
instruments in which he took a keen interest.[51] Rarely did
Cameron include tools of the trade in her photographs, but
Joachim and his violin were inseparable.[52]

It might seem surprising that an outside photographer was
allowed to set up operations within the museum. Sir Henry
Cole, the director, was both a subject and an ardent supporter of Cameron, and gave her space within the building
to set up a small studio.[53]

[49] "Monday Popular Concerts," *The Pall Mall Gazette*, 18 February 1868.
[50] "Art and Literary Gossip," *Manchester Times*, 11 April 1868.
[51] Its most important collection of musical instruments was acquired from
Carl Engel (1818–1882) of Hanover, author of *A Descriptive Catalogue of the
Musical Instruments in the South Kensington Museum* (London: Her Majesty's
Stationary Office, 1874).
[52] "She had little interest in sociological data, details of clothing, tools of
trades." Phyllis Rose, "Milkmaid Madonnas: An Appreciation of Cameron's Portraits of Women," in Sylvia Wolf, *Julia Margaret Cameron's Women*
(New Haven: Yale University Press, 1998), p. 13.
[53] Four days after Cameron took this portrait, she wrote to Cole, thanking
him for lending her some of John Pouncy's "improved" photographic
prints. But she had to confess, "[I] cannot say that I think the artistic character of photography is preserved … for anything so delicate as a portrait
the shining glazed surface destroys the pleasure by giving a sticking plaster
look & I think that even in oil paintings any thick coating of varnish is a
great injury to the effect. It is the dull quiet surface of a photograph however rich in tone & tint it may be, that constitutes I think the harmony of
the work …." Letter, Cameron to Cole, 7 April 1868. Archives, Victoria
and Albert Museum.

Herr Joachim

Julia Margaret Cameron

16. *The Dream*
Albumen print from a wet collodion negative, April 1869.
30.3 x 24.7 cm. Provenance: Jackson-Vaughan family,
by descent. Cox & Ford no. 258

In her 1874 *Annals of My Glass House*, Cameron praised Mary Hillier as "One of the most beautiful and constant of my models, and in every manner of form has her face been reproduced, yet never has it been felt that the grace of the fashion of it has perished."[54] Mary Hillier was the parlor maid in Cameron's household (see item no. 5, p. 20).

On some prints of this photograph, Cameron inscribed the line, "Me thought I saw my late espoused saint," a quote from John Milton's Sonnet XXIII. The renowned poet had been totally blind for some time when his beloved second wife, Katherine Woodcock, died from the effects of childbirth in 1658. In the poem, she came back to him in a dream:

> Methought I saw my late espoused Saint
> Brought to me like Alcestis from the grave,
> . . .
> Her face was veil'd, yet to my fancied sight,
> Love, sweetness, goodness in her person shin'd
> So clear, as in no face with more delight.
> But O as to embrace me she enclin'd,
> I wak'd, she fled, and day brought back my night.[55]

At some point in printing this fine image, Cameron glumly noted: "negative injured."[56] Perhaps she was referring to the two dark fingerprints in the lower right, where the collodion was affected. These could have easily have been retouched in printing, so it is possible that the negative suffered even more drastic damage after this print was made.

[54] Transcribed in Helmut Gernsheim, *Julia Margaret Cameron: Her Life and Photographic Work* (London: The Fountain Press, 1948), pp. 67–73. Cameron wrote this short manuscript in 1874; it was first published in a gallery catalogue in 1889 and received a wider readership when it appeared in *The Photographic Journal* in 1927.
[55] Milton's blindness returned upon awakening from the dream. In Euripides' *Alcestis*, Hercules rescues the dead heroine from the underworld and restores her to her adoring husband.
[56] Cox & Ford, p. 209

JULIA MARGARET CAMERON

17. *Sir Leslie Stephen*
Albumen print from a wet collodion negative, circa 1872.
35.1 x 26.8 cm mounted on 38.4 x 27.6 cm card, ruled
in gilt at bottom. Inscription in ink "From life / Julia
Margaret Cameron / The Cameron Studio 70 Mortimer
St. W" on mount. Title in ink "Leslie Stephen" on mount
verso. Provenance: Jackson-Vaughan family, by descent.
Cox & Ford no. 759

In 1859, triumphantly making the first crossing of a spectacular pass in the Alps, the pioneering mountaineer Leslie Stephen looked upon the majestic sweep of the glacier and the view beyond it, which he called "some of the noblest mountains in Europe." However, returning a decade later, he found that much of this scene existed solely within his memory—in reality, two mountains cut off a large part of the view that he so vividly recalled. He was untroubled by his memory and unapologetic for his inaccurate description, declaring, "He who sees only what is before his eyes sees the worst part of every view."[57] Nothing could better describe Julia Margaret Cameron's photographs, especially this portrait of Stephen. The background, the barrier between the sitter and the world, is peeled away, giving the impression that he sees beyond merely what is before his eyes.

In 1878, Leslie Stephen (1832–1904) became the second husband of Cameron's niece and goddaughter, Julia Duckworth, born Julia Jackson (see item no. 18, p. 46) and their two daughters became the writer Virginia Woolf and the artist Vanessa Bell. A man of almost unbelievably diverse talents, he balanced being a founding member of the Alpine Club and the founding editor of the *Dictionary of National Biography*. Stephen trained as a clergyman, but, swayed by Darwin's writings, later became an atheist.

This portrait was taken well before Stephen's marriage to Cameron's goddaughter. His first wife was Harriet Marian (1840–1875), a daughter of William Makepeace Thackeray, and through the Thackeray household Stephen met many literary and artistic figures. His father had been a close friend of Cameron's frequent sitter Henry Taylor, so it is not surprising that he caught the photographer's eye. After the death of his first wife, Stephen moved in with his sister-in-law in London's Kensington Gardens, where the recently widowed Julia Duckworth was their neighbor.

[57] Leslie Stephen, *The Playground of Europe* (London: Longman, Green, & Co., 1871), pp. 170–171.

18. *A Beautiful Vision, Julia Duckworth*
Carbon print, June 1872. 33.5 x 25.4 cm mounted on
50.7 x 41.5 cm board. Engraved label "H. H. Hay Cameron
70 Mortimer Street, W" on mount verso. Provenance:
Jackson-Vaughan family, by descent. Cox & Ford no. 316

> Her loveliness with shame and with surprise
> Froze my swift speech; she turning on my face
> The star-like sorrows of immortal eyes,
> Spoke slowly in her place
> —Lord Tennyson, *A Dream of Fair Women*, 1832

Cameron inscribed one print of this image: "The Star like sorrows of Immortal Eyes." Another print, formerly owned by Alvin Langdon Coburn and now in the Royal Photographic Society Collection at the National Media Museum, is titled "A Beautiful Vision June 1872."

The subject was Cameron's niece and goddaughter, born Julia Jackson (1846–1895) in Calcutta. Throughout her life she was a frequent sitter and inspiration for her aunt's photographs. Sylvia Wolf noted that, "While much of the energy in Cameron's portraits of famous men derives from an appreciation of the mind and spirit, her portraits of women reflect a broader inquiry into human nature and into the expressive possibilities of photography."[58] Stephanie Lipscomb observed that, in spite of the frequency of her sittings, "unlike most of her other female subjects, whom Cameron portrayed as characters from biblical, classical, or literary sources, Julia was almost always represented as herself, simply and eloquently, without pretense."[59]

Cameron inscribed another print of this negative: "A Study & A Portrait / My own cherished Niece and God Child / Julia Duckworth / a widow at 24." Julia's first husband, the barrister Herbert Duckworth, died in 1870, after only three years of marriage. After a long widowhood, she was married for a second time, to Sir Leslie Stephen (see item no. 17, p. 44).[60] She was the mother of Vanessa Bell and Virginia Woolf.

This is a carbon print, a form of photographic printing that left an image created in carbon or permanent pigments. As part of her preparations for going to Ceylon in 1875, Cameron paid the Autotype Company in London the considerable sum of two guineas each to create master transparencies from some of her personally selected negatives. Carbon printing required this interpositive, and it was natural at this stage to retouch any defects carried over from the original negative. The printing process was exacting, but, in the hands of the accomplished Autotype Company, the results were flawless, and particularly richly textured, prints of undoubted permanence. Barring some future accident, this particular *Beautiful Vision* will always remain as beautiful as the day it was printed.

[58] Sylvia Wolf, *Julia Margaret Cameron's Women* (New Haven: Yale University Press, 1998), p. 24.
[59] Stephanie Lipscomb, "Sitter's Biographies," in Sylvia Wolf, op. cit., p. 222.
[60] A typographical error in the *catalogue raisonné* has her remarry in 1870. See Cox & Ford, p. 515.

JULIA MARGARET CAMERON

19. *"Alice"*
Albumen print from a collodion negative, September 1872.
28.4 x 10.7 cm mounted on 58.5 x 46.5 cm card, ruled in
gilt. Signed, titled, and inscribed in ink "From life / Registered Photograph Copyright," with Colnaghi blindstamp
on mount. Provenance: Christopher Wood; Daniel Wolf;
Leonard / Peil Collection. Cox & Ford no. 361

The little girl of *Alice's Adventures in Wonderland* is so firmly
fixed in the public's mind that it is difficult to imagine Alice
Pleasance Liddell (1852–1934) as a grown woman. When
Cameron took this photograph, a decade after Alice's famous
rowboat ride with Charles Dodgson, the young girl had
matured. Under the pen name Lewis Carroll, Dodgson had
just published the sequel to *Alice in Wonderland*, titled
Through the Looking-Glass, and What Alice Found There. Anne
Clark observes that "underlying the charm and wit ... is an
intense preoccupation with transience of beauty, with death
and decay, and loss of maidenhood."[61]

It was not entirely by accident that Alice came to be
photographed by Cameron. The Liddell family had tired of
their usual Welsh vacations, and they knew of Freshwater
through their friend the poet Sir Henry Taylor. Alice's
father's cousin Adolphus Liddell began spending the sum-
mers at Cowes on a friend's schooner, and was photographed
by Cameron. The Liddells' visits to the Isle of Wight soon
became a regular event, as did being photographed by
Cameron.

There were rumors that a potential match was in the off-
ing between Alice and Prince Leopold, a son of Queen Victoria. However uncommon her youth had been, Alice was
still a commoner, and if potential for this match ever existed,
it did not materialize. In 1880, Alice married another Oxford
student, Reginald Hargreaves, a wealthy cricketer and mag-
istrate, and she became better known as a society hostess than
as an adventurer.

[61] Anne Clark, *The Real Alice: Lewis Carroll's Dream Child* (New York: Stein
and Day, 1982), p. 128.

From life Registered Photograph Copyright Julia Margaret Cameron

Alice

20. *"Lorina, Edith, and Alice Liddell"*
Albumen print from a wet collodion negative,
August 1872. 34.5 x 28.3 cm mounted on 58.5 x 46.5 cm
card, ruled in gilt. Signed, titled, dated, and inscribed in
ink "From life FreshWater," with Colnaghi blindstamp on
mount. Provenance: Jackson-Vaughan family, by descent.
Cox & Ford no. 363

These are the famous daughters of Dr. Henry George Liddell, dean of Christ Church at Oxford. On the right is Alice Pleasance (see item no. 19, p. xx) the namesake of Lewis Carroll's *Alice's Adventures in Wonderland*. In the middle is her younger sister Edith (1854–1876), the basis for the character of the Eaglet, and the probable model for the illustrations in Carroll's book. On the left is her older sister Lorina "Ina" (1849–1930), the basis for the character of Lory. These three sisters grew up very close within the larger Liddell family. In Cameron's photograph, they are no longer the little girls who inspired Carroll, but rather three graces. In contrast to the long-haired girls he photographed, they have adopted grown-up hairstyles, possibly inspired by the latest illustrations in the *Englishwoman's Domestic Magazine*. They have also adopted the fashion of sisters dressing alike, which had recently been made popular by the Princess of Wales, and are wearing what was known as the "artistic dress" of the Pre-Raphaelites.

Perhaps Cameron dug into one of her trunks, selecting a voluminous Indian silk dress, bordered in *Zardozi*[62] and split it into three costumes. Embroidery edges the collars and the sleeves, and apparently gilt metal decorations stitched onto bands cross the waists.[63] At least two of the sisters attended an entertainment at Freshwater on 15 August, and it is possible these costumes were produced for that.[64] It is also conceivable that they were for one of Cameron's dramatic presentations at Freshwater. Whatever the basis of the dresses, this is one of Cameron's more dynamic group arrangements, with each young woman acting out her independence, even through the sisterly bond between them is clear. One contemporary observer said of Cameron's photographs, "In her composition pieces, she has evinced rare faculties of dealing with the emotions of her sitters. She does not take them anyhow, but draws them out, and induces in them such a condition of mind and feeling as gives rise to a vivid and pictorial expression of feature."[65] This is the only known print of this image, a close but more active variant of a Cameron photograph in the Royal Photographic Society Collection.[66]

Eighteen months after Cameron captured this trio, Lorina married a wealthy Scot, William Baillie Skene, who stayed in Oxford and eventually became treasurer of Christ Church. Edith tragically developed peritonitis and died four years after this portrait, on the eve of her wedding. Alice married in 1880.

[62] Persian for the handicraft of decorating cloth with gold and silver threads. During her long residence in India, Cameron collected such fabrics, and examples of enormous silk dresses from the period are known in other collections.
[63] I am indebted to Charlotte Gere, author of *Artistic Circles: Design and Decoration in the Aesthetic Movement* (London: V&A Publishing, 2010), for personal communications exploring their dress.
[64] One of Cameron's neighbors at West Hall, Freshwater, was Admiral Richard Crozier. His sister the philanthropist Frances Margaret Crozier threw a ball there for her nephew the naval seaman Pearson Frank Crozier, before his departure for the East. Mrs. Liddell, two Misses Liddell, and Mrs. Cameron were among the guests. "Festivities at Freshwater," *The Hampshire Advertiser,* 17 August 1872, p. 8.
[65] "Mrs. Cameron's Photographs," *The Intellectual Observer; Review of Natural History, Microscopic Research, and Recreative Science,* v. 11 no. 1, February 1867, pp. 31–32.
[66] Cox & Ford no. 364.

From life Fresh Water August 1872 Julia Margaret Cameron

Lorina Edith and Alice Liddell

21. *"King Lear allotting his Kingdom to his Daughters"*
Albumen print from a wet collodion negative, September
1872. 33.9 x 28.7 cm mounted on 58.5 x 46.4 cm card,
ruled in gilt. Signed, titled, dated, and inscribed in ink
"From life Registered photograph copy right / FreshWater
/ What shall Cordelia do / Love and be silent / For dear
Adeline / from Aunt Julia," with Colnaghi blindstamp on
mount. Provenance: Jackson-Vaughan family, by descent.
Cox & Ford no. 1141

Shakespeare's tragedy plunges the aging King Lear into a
morass of misunderstanding and betrayal. At the opening of
the play, Lear rejects his illegitimate son and decides to divide
his kingdom among his three daughters; each will get a division in proportion to the eloquence of her profession of love
for him. The two older married daughters, Goneril and
Regan, are grandly eloquent and totally insincere in their
pronouncements. Lear's youngest and favorite daughter,
Cordelia, the only one who actually loves him, makes no
declaration, feeling that mere words cannot adequately
express her love. Lear does not understand this, and in his
rage divides his kingdom between Goneril and Regan, who
in turn mock their naive little sister. In the end, they turn on
their father, and then on each other. Caught up in family in-
trigue and war, the play ends with the dying King Lear holding the lifeless body of his one faithful daughter in his arms.

Cameron places the two wicked daughters plotting together behind their father's back. The modest and virtuous
Cordelia is dressed in virginal white, emphasized by a band
of light within the print. At first, one might think that this
was the result of the combination printing of two negatives,
but close examination shows that not to be the case. Since
this division is present in all known prints, maybe it was a
defect in the negative that Cameron accepted for its symbolic
nature, or perhaps it was an effect she introduced inten-
tionally.

The sisters here were real-life sisters, Lorina, Edith and
Alice (see items no. 19 & 20, pp. 48 & 50), the daughters of
Henry Liddell, and best known for their roles in *Alice's
Adventures in Wonderland*.

King Lear was played by Cameron's much older husband,
Charles Hay Cameron (1795–1880). A lawyer, he was instru-
mental in creating India's legal system in the 1840s. Tennyson's biographer considered him "a first-rate classic, and he
and the Laureate engage in an animated discussion about the
respective merits of certain Greek and Latin writers, and the
peculiarities of their styles."[67] Her husband's intimate famil-
iarity with her world of legends undoubtedly lent moral support if not actual substance to Cameron's photography, but
his physical appearance was an asset as well. Commenting on
her photographs of him in a similar role, Cameron said that
she would have had to wait a "hundred years before I could
find such another Merlin as my husband."[68]

Charles Cameron happened to develop the appearance
useful for this photograph while away at their coffee plantations in Ceylon. On his return, Alfred Tennyson "who had
seen him last a clean-shaven man, started back in astonish-
ment at the vision of the long silvery beard which Mr.
Cameron had grown during his absence, crying out as he
did so, 'Why, Cameron, you have dipped your chin in the
moonlight since I saw you last!'—a compliment worthy of a
great poet."[69]

[67] Henry James Jennings, *Lord Tennyson; a Biographical Sketch* (London:
Chatto and Windus, 1884), p. 203.
[68] Letter, Cameron to Francis W. Fox of the Bristol Art Society. 15 December 1876. The Metropolitan Museum of Art, New York.
[69] Raymond Blathwayt, "How Celebrities Have Been Photographed," *The
Windsor Magazine*, v. 2, December 1895, p. 642.

King Lear allotting his kingdom to his Daughters

"What shall Cordelia do"
"Love and be silent"

22. *I see a hand you cannot see*
Albumen print from a wet collodion negative, 14 May 1873. 37.7 x 24.1 cm on 38.7 x 27.1 cm paper, untrimmed, mounted on 38.8 x 30.2 cm card. Signed two times and dated in the negative. Provenance: Jackson-Vaughan family, by descent. Cox & Ford no. 382

Perhaps Cameron had been reading Sir Walter Scott's recently republished *Rob Roy*, in which the bard introduces a chapter with a quotation from Thomas Tickell's 1725 ballad "Lucy and Colin." Cast off for a rival with three times her wealth, Lucy realizes that she is about to die:

> I hear a voice you cannot hear
> Which fondly whispers 'stay'
> I see a hand you cannot see
> which beckons me away[70]

Her dying wish is to be taken to Colin's wedding, and when he sees her lifeless body he also dies, and they lie buried together.

Cameron has carefully arranged her picture, first blocking out the background with a dark cloth (held up by a pole on the upper left) and then framing her subject with hanging flowers and patterns on the cloth, as if an ornamental capital letter in an illuminated manuscript. The defects in the negative's collodion—imperfections which Cameron embraced rather than struggled against—add to the otherworldly quality of the image.

This untrimmed print offers a wonderful opportunity to consider Cameron's struggles not only with the collodion on glass negative process but also with albumen printing. The frilly edge at the top of the negative betrays a collodion film that is trying to separate from the glass, a problem she somehow avoided at first with beginner's luck, but one that so seriously affected her later work that she appealed to the members of the Photographic Society for help. The white spots on the upper right and at the bottom of the print are areas where her light-sensitive silver solution did not reach the albumen; it's possible they are air bubbles, but more likely they are result of trying to quickly and evenly coat the paper with a sponge. The negative is hastily placed at an angle on the paper, fortunately still capturing its entirety.[71]

The sitter is Emily Peacock, and nothing is presently known of her or her sister Mary. They may have been visitors to the Isle of Wight,[72] or even guests of the Camerons, for Julia inscribed one portrait of Emily "Angel in the House." In the period between May 1873 to May 1875, Cameron is known to have taken ten portraits of Emily alone, two with Mary, and a study of the two sisters with Cameron's daughter-in-law Annie Cameron, née Chinery (b. ca. 1851).[73] "Mrs. Cameron was an indefatigable worker, and she utilized every one and anything that came to her notice. If she needed a model for a certain picture and chanced to see a fair visitor in Freshwater who pleased her fancy, she would unhesitatingly pounce upon her and, making friends at once, escort her delighted prey to her 'glass house.' "[74]

[70] Scott quoted it at the head of chapter 17 in *Waverley, or 'tis Sixty Years Since* (Edinburgh: Adam and Charles Black, 1866), p. 573.
[71] An insightful analysis with an annotated reproduction of a Cameron negative of George Warde Norman is given by Julian Cox in Cox & Ford, pp. 48–49.
[72] With an intensive study of local newspapers, this just might be traced, for newspapers of the period often tracked the comings and goings of the chattering classes. For example, "The Fashionable List" for the week of 7 March 1874 listed a "Mrs G. Peacocke & family" staying at the Arabin Lodge in Castle Street in nearby Ryde. *Isle of Wight Observer,* 7 March 1874, p. 2.
[73] Illustrated in Cox & Ford, nos. 372–385.
[74] Alvin Langdon Coburn, "The Old Masters of Photography," *Century Magazine,* v. 90, October 1915, p. 916.

JULIA MARGARET CAMERON

23. *"Cupid escaped from his Mother"*
Albumen print from a wet collodion negative, 1873.
34.8 x 28.0 cm, arched top, mounted on 58.5 x 46.5 cm
card, ruled in gilt. Signed, titled, dated, and inscribed in
ink "From Life / Registered photograph copyright /
Freshwater / See Theocritus / A gift to the givers of
my Camera from their grateful Mother," with Colnaghi
blindstamp on mount. Provenance: Hansen Collection.
Cox & Ford no. 899

> As Cupid from his mother Venus stray'd
> Thus, crying him aloud, the goddess said –
> 'If anyone a wandering Cupid see
> The little fugitive belongs to me'
> —Theocritus, *Idyllia of Moschus*[75]

Cameron's imagination was alive with mythological images, and she often constructed photographs that were akin to her elaborate stage designs. Not everyone was impressed with this side of her work. The irascible George Bernard Shaw, reviewing the 1889 Cameron retrospective for the radical newspaper *The Star*, was clearly confounded: "While the portraits of Herschel, Tennyson and Carlyle beat hollow anything I have ever seen, right on the same wall, and virtually in the same frame, there are photographs of children with no clothes on, or else the underclothes by way of propriety, with palpably paper wings, most inartistically grouped and artlessly labeled as angels, saints or fairies. No-one would imagine that the artist who produced the marvelous Carlyle would have produced such childish trivialities."[76]

Yet this constructed portrait rises above the artificiality of some of its companions. Cameron has used the fantastically effective framing device of draping her open-weave shawl near the lens. It becomes so out of focus and magnified that it loses its physicality and becomes ethereal. The child, in spite of the artificial wings, is genuine in pose and pensive expression. It is a beautiful photograph, an image that one can love even without feeling the sting of Cupid's arrow. Charles Millard, considering Cameron's photographs for Tennyson's *The Idylls of the King*, observed: "The fact remains, however, that this literal and literary interest was not the determinant of her vision but its servant, and that her wish was to project a mood, if possible one emanating from the most subtly shaded human emotions, rather than to enumerate."[77]

The sitter is possibly Daisy Taylor.[78] Cameron took at least seven portraits of her in 1872 and 1873 and included her in five group pictures in 1874. Nothing else is known about her—thus far there is no established connection with the several Daisy Taylors from England of about the right age. Daisy is also a common nickname for Margaret (from the French word for a type of daisy, *marguerite*).

Cameron's inscription on this print, "A gift to the givers of my Camera from their grateful Mother," is dedicated to her daughter Julia and her husband, Charles Lloyd Norman. Cameron, profoundly depressed, had visited them when her husband returned to Ceylon. In December 1863, they gave her an 11 x 9 inch wet-plate camera with all the necessary accessories. They said, "It may amuse you, Mother, to try to photograph during your solitude at Freshwater."[79] It did far more than amuse. Cameron recalled, "The gift from those I loved so tenderly added more and more impulse to my deeply seated love of the beautiful, and from the first moment I handled my lens with a tender ardour, and it has become to be as a living thing, with voice and memory and creative vigour."[80]

[75] "The Stray Cupid," in Richard Polwhele, *The Idyllia, Epigrams, and Fragments, of Theocritus, Bion, and Moschus* (Chiswick: C. Whittingham, 1822), p. 143. Theocritus flourished in the 3rd century BCE.
[76] Quoted from Helmut Gernsheim, *Julia Margaret Cameron: Her Life and Photographic Work* (London: Gordon Fraser, 1975), p. 67.
[77] Charles W. Millard, "Julia Margaret Cameron and Tennyson's *Idylls of the King*," Harvard Library Bulletin, v. 21 no. 2, April 1973, p. 200.
[78] See Cox & Ford no. 899.
[79] See Joanne Lukitsh, "Before 1864: Julia Margaret Cameron's Early Work in Photography," in Cox & Ford, pp. 95–105.
[80] Transcribed in Helmut Gernsheim, *Julia Margaret Cameron: Her Life and Photographic Work* (London: The Fountain Press, 1948), pp. 67–68, revised edition (London: Gordon Fraser, 1975), p. 180.

Copyright Julia Margaret Cameron 1873
Cupid escaped from his mother

24. *She Walks in Beauty* [81]
Albumen print from a wet collodion negative, copyrighted
6 June 1874. 33.3 x 25.7 cm. Provenance: Jackson-Vaughan
family, by descent. Cox & Ford no. 173

> She walks in beauty, like the night
> Of cloudless climes and starry skies;
> And all that's best of dark and bright
> Meet in her aspect and her eyes:
> —Lord Byron, *She walks in beauty*, 1814

Cameron left us a clue to her working technique here, one
that was helped by the nature of her sitter, Isabel Bateman, a
professional stage actress. Almost everything in this image is
relatively sharp, from the figure to the backdrop of leaves.
However, two small dangles at her waist are still in blurred
motion. This leads us to assume that at the moment immediately before the picture was taken, the actress drew herself
up into position, as she would have just before addressing
an audience. She held that pose, and the dangles continued
to sway.

Born in Cincinnati, Ohio, Isabel Emilie Bateman
(1854–1934) was the youngest daughter of a Baltimore actor
and his English actress wife. Isabel's two older sisters Ellen
and Kate were childhood stars in America. Isabel's own stage
career began in New York, but gained momentum after her
debut in London in 1865. Her parents leased the Lyceum
Theatre to showcase her talents. Isabel's flamboyant father,
H. L. Bateman, died a year after this photograph was taken.
Her mother, Sidney Frances, lost control of the theater soon
after, but Isabel continued to star in Lyceum productions for
many years. In 1898 she left the stage for a new role, joining
the Community of St. Mary the Virgin, Wantage, Berkshire,
where she again took the lead, becoming reverend mother
general.

[81] The title is from the inscription on a carbon print of this image in the
Royal Photographic Society Collection, the National Media Museum,
Bradford.

JULIA MARGARET CAMERON

25. *"Andrew K. Hichens"*
Albumen print from a wet collodion negative, October
1874. 36.1 x 28.6 cm mounted on 58.1 x 46.4 cm card,
ruled in gilt. Signed, titled, dated, and inscribed in ink
"From life / registered photograph copy right / FreshWater
/ My Birthday Gift to sweet Adeline / The most excellent
and delightful of Men / A Man May can love for ever,"
with Colnaghi blindstamp on mount. Provenance: Jackson-
Vaughan family, by descent. Cox & Ford no. 679

In this compelling portrait, we see the face of a man we
might expect to meet today. The swirl of the cape echoes the
roundness of the cap, neatly enclosing the face in a contrast-
ing space. A light source high and behind traces a fine high-
light around the brim of the hat, lifting the subject out of the
background, and a strong counterpoint of light illuminates
his face.

Judging by her inscription, Cameron felt quite strongly
about the subject, Andrew Kinsman Hichens (1833–1906), a
leading broker in the London stock exchange. He had
recently married Julia's relative, Mary Emily "May" Prinsep
(1853–1931). Although he was a very successful business-
man, Hitchens had another side to him that was probably
what appealed to Julia. His death brought all the expected
obituaries in financial journals, and one in the prestigious
Musical Times: "Mr. Hichens, a well-known stockbroker and
held in the highest esteem in the financial life of the City,
took a keen and practical interest in music, and was a gener-
ous supporter ... he will be greatly missed in the business and
artistic circles which were favoured by his genial presence."[82]

[82] "Obituary," *The Musical Times*, v. 47 no.764, 1 October 1906, p. 688.
Hitchens predeceased Cameron's niece and May then became the second
wife of Hallam Tennyson, 2nd Baron Tennyson (1852–1928), the son of
Cameron's poet laureate friend, and later Governor-General of Australia.

LARRY J. SCHAAF, an independent photographic historian based in Baltimore, Maryland, was elected the 2005 Slade Professor of Fine Art at Oxford University. Dr. Schaaf is the founder and Director of *The Correspondence of William Henry Fox Talbot* project, originated at Glasgow and now based at De Montfort University; full transcriptions of 10,000 of Talbot's letters have been published online and are continually updated at http://foxtalbot.dmu.ac.uk. A companion project currently in development by Schaaf is the *Catalogue Raisonné of photographs by William Henry Fox Talbot and his circle*. This online resource will encompass the nearly 25,000 Talbot negatives and prints known worldwide. Some of Schaaf's books include *Out of the Shadows: Herschel, Talbot & the Invention of Photography* (Yale University Press); *The Photographic Art of William Henry Fox Talbot* (Princeton University Press); and *In Focus: William Henry Fox Talbot Photographs from the J. Paul Getty Museum*. He contributed the "Dictionary of Calotypists" in collaboration with Roger Taylor in *Impressed by Light: British Photographs from Paper Negatives, 1840–1860* (Yale University Press, in association with The Metropolitan Museum of Art).

Front cover: No. 18
Back cover: No. 23

ISBN 1–892535–31–9

Research and text by Larry J. Schaaf
Assistance by Valentina Branchini, Shelley Dowell and Jennifer Parkinson
Designed by Peter A. Andersen
Digital photography by A. C. Cooper Ltd.
Color separations and printing on
PhoeniXmotion Xantur coated paper
by Meridian Printing